Cognitive Restructuring
for Addiction Workbook

Developed by Terence T. Gorski

Based on the GORSKI-CENAPS® Model

CENAPS®
6147 Deltona Blvd.
Spring Hill, FL 34606
Phone: (352) 596-8000
Fax: (352) 596-8002
E-mail: *info@cenaps.com*

For professional guides and recovery workbooks related to this training manual call 1-800-767-8181 or visit *www.relapse.org*. Updated clinical materials are available at Terry Gorski's Clinical Development Web site: *www.tgorski.com*. Network with other users of this material at *www.relapse.net*.

Additional copies may be obtained from the publisher:

Herald House/Independence Press
1001 West Walnut
P.O. Box 390
Independence, MO 64051-0390
Phone: 1-800-767-8181 or 816-521-3015
Fax: 816-521-3066
Web site: *www.relapse.org*

Printed in the United States of America
ISBN 0-8309-1128-6

Contents

Introduction

This workbook will teach you how to use a recovery system called Cognitive Restructuring for Addiction (CRFA). This system teaches a series of five progressive skills that are critical to addiction recovery. These skills are:

1. Addiction-Focused Problem Solving
2. Managing Addictive Thoughts
3. Managing Addictive Feelings
4. Managing Addictive Behaviors
5. Integrating Personal Reactions

Let's take a minute to briefly describe each of these skills. The rest of the workbook will clearly explain each of the skills and give exercises to help you master them.

1. **Addiction-Focused Problem Solving:** The first skill is *Addiction-Focused Problem Solving*. Recovery from addiction doesn't mean that you become problem free. It means that you learn how to deal with your problems in a sober and responsible way. The first cognitive restructuring for addiction exercise will show you a process for identifying, clarifying, and solving personal problems in a way that keeps the relationship between the problem and your addiction clearly in focus.

2. **Managing Addictive Thinking:** The second skill is *Managing Addictive Thinking*. In the process of getting and staying addicted, we tend to develop habits of addictive thinking that make us want to use alcohol and other drugs. Addictive thinking operates on two levels. First, addictive thinking causes unnecessary pain and problems. Second, the addictive thinking convinces you that the only way to manage the pain or solve the problems is to start using alcohol or other drugs.

   These addictive thoughts are cunning, baffling, and powerful. They tend to pop into our minds when we least expect them. Once the addictive thinking process starts, it's hard to stop. The addictive thoughts seem to take on a life of their own.

   Cognitive Restructuring for Addiction shows you how to identify and manage the addictive thoughts that can cause unnecessary pain and problems and convince you that it's OK to use alcohol or other drugs to manage the pain and solve the problems.

3. **Managing Addictive Feelings:** The third skill is *Managing Addictive Feelings*. Addicted people tend to mismanage their feelings and emotions. They block, exaggerate, or distort their feelings. When we block our feelings, we push them down and refuse to acknowledge that we are feeling anything. When we exaggerate our feelings, we think thoughts that keep making our feelings more intense. When we distort our feelings, we think thoughts that turn one feeling into another feeling. We can, for example, turn fear into anger by thinking thoughts that make us mad at the people or things that are scaring us. Unless we learn effective emotional management, we can start to feel so bad that drinking and drugging seems like a good choice. *Cognitive Restructuring for Addiction* teaches you an effective system for managing feelings and emotions in recovery.

4. **Managing Addictive Behaviors:** The fourth skill is *Managing Addictive Behaviors*. The human brain is a habit-forming computer. We start turning anything that we do more than once into an automatic habit. Once we develop habits, we can do things automatically without thinking about them. This frees us to think about more important things.

When we become addicted, we develop a wide range of habitual behaviors that has only one purpose—to put us around people, places, events, and things that support our drinking and drug use. These habitual behaviors are called drug-seeking behaviors. In order to recover from addiction, we must learn to identify and change these drug-seeking behaviors.

5. **Integrating Personal Reactions:** The fifth skill is to make the cognitive restructuring for addiction process a part of whom you are. To do this, you need to develop the habit of using addiction-focused problem solving whenever you face any problem in your life. It also means learning how to get in the habit of consciously monitoring your thoughts, feelings, urges, actions, and social reactions. This last exercise will give you a simple format for practicing this process on a daily basis until it becomes habitual.

Now it's time to get busy learning the Cognitive Restructuring for Addiction Process.

1 Addiction-Focused Problem Solving

1-1 What Is Addiction-Focused Problem Solving?

When you recover from addiction, you don't become problem free. You learn how to deal with your problems in a sober and responsible way.

- *Sober problem solving* is the ability to solve problems without having to use alcohol or other drugs.
- *Responsible problem solving* is the ability to identify and solve problems in a way that is fair to all involved.

If you want to stay in recovery, you need to use *addiction-focused problem solving*.

1-2 How Problems Are Related to Addiction

Once you become addicted, all your problems are related in some way to your addiction. A particular problem can be related to your addiction in one of four ways:

- **You used your drinking and drugging to deal with the problem:** You had a serious problem and used alcohol and other drugs in an attempt to solve the problem. Sometimes it may have worked. At other times it didn't.
- **The problem was caused by your addiction:** The problem may have been caused by your addiction. In other words, if you had never started drinking or drugging, you never would have developed the problem. Examples of this would be getting arrested for drunk driving or drug charges, or getting divorced because your drinking and drugging became intolerable to your spouse.
- **The problem was complicated by your addiction:** The problem may have been complicated by your addiction. In other words, you would have had the problem whether or not you ever started drinking and drugging, but your addiction made the problem worse. You may have been in a dead-end job before you got addicted, but your addiction created new job problems that trapped you there. You might have been in a dysfunctional marriage, and your drinking and drugging pushed your spouse to divorce you.
- **The problem increases your risk of relapse:** The problem can cause so much pain and disruption in your life that you may choose to use alcohol or drugs to manage the pain and escape from the problem.

All of your problems are related to addiction! This is because any problem that you have can activate addictive thinking and make you want to start using alcohol and or other drugs. If you don't believe this, then you're in high risk for having a relapse. Why? Because if you don't believe that a problem is related to your addiction, you probably won't use your recovery program to try to solve it. You'll go back to your old ways of solving problems. As you work hard at solving the problem, it's easy to lose the addiction focus that you've built into your life, get sidetracked, and fall into old addictive ways of thinking. This leads to the use of addictive behaviors followed by relapse. Addiction-

7

focused problem solving allows you to solve a wide variety of life problems while keeping recovery from addiction as your top priority.

Addiction-focused problem solving follows a number of steps that can be learned and consistently used to promote recovery and prevent relapse.

1-3 Step 1: Identifying a Problem

Addiction-focused problem solving begins by identifying a problem. You can do this by asking yourself a simple question—"What's going on in my life that's making me unhappy?" It's important to write down the answer to that question. Your answer should begin with the words: "One problem that's making me unhappy is: _____. Let's give it a try. Think about something that's making you unhappy in your life.

> 1. **Problem:** What's going on in my life that's making me unhappy?
> One problem that's making me unhappy is . . .
>
> _____
>
> _____

1-4 Step 2: Identifying When the Problem Started

The next step is to figure out when the problem started. All problems have a history. The most serious problems that we experience in our recovery tend to be those that keep coming back. One person, for example, said his problem was that he had a bad fight with his wife. After thinking about when the problem really started, he realized that he had been fighting with his wife for many years. He could see that the real problem wasn't the most recent fight. The real problem was the fact that he and his wife had serious and long disagreements about many important things. When these things would come up, they'd argue, resolve nothing, and then pretend the problem didn't exist. As a result, the problem would keep coming up again. Each time they argued, he would get upset, feel guilty, and blame his wife. To handle these feelings, he'd go out and start drinking.

Addiction-focused problem solving is based on the belief that if problems are identified and clarified they can be resolved. In other words, they can be permanently solved so that they don't keep coming up over and over.

So let's take a minute to clarify when the problem you just identified really began. You do this by answering the question: "When did this first become a problem?"

> 2. **When the Problem Started:** When did this first become a problem?
> This first became a problem when . . .
>
> _____
>
> _____

8

1-5 Step 3: Past Attempts to Solve the Problem

This leads us to the third question: "What have you done in the past to try to solve this problem?" Most people try to solve their problems on their own. They won't ask for help until they've tried everything they know how to try. So, it's important to think about what you've tried to do to solve the problem and what happened as a result. Did your efforts to solve the problem make the problem better or make it worse? You can make the answer to this question specific by challenging yourself to identify the three most important things you've done in the past to try to solve this problem and what happened as a result. Let's give it a try.

3. **Past Attempts to Solve the Problem:** What are the three most important things that you've done in the past to try to solve this problem, and what happened as a result?

A.   The first thing I did to try and solve this problem was . . .

_____

_____

As a result of doing this, the problem . . .

Got better   Stayed the same   Got worse   Explain:

_____

_____

B.   The second thing I did to try to solve this problem was . . .

_____

_____

As a result of doing this, the problem . . .
Got better   Stayed the same   Got worse   Explain:

_____

_____

C.   The third thing I did to try to solve this problem was . . .

_____

_____

As a result of doing this, the problem . . .
Got better   Stayed the same   Got worse   Explain:

_____

_____

1-6 Step 4: Identifying the Motivating Event

Most of us struggle with our problems for a long time before we become willing to ask for help. We usually go through a cycle of ineffective problem solving. We actively try to solve the problem, fail, and then try to avoid the problem by pretending that it doesn't exist or by convincing ourselves that it isn't important.

When the problem keeps causing us pain, we try to solve it again, fail, and once again lapse into denial. This cycle continues until we experience a motivating event. Something happens that forces us to ask for help. We may hit bottom and decide for ourselves that we need help. Or something might happen that causes other people to force us to get the help we need.

So, what's your motivating event? Why did you decide to ask for help now? Why didn't you do it yesterday? Why didn't you put it off until tomorrow? Did something happen that made you want to ask for help? Did something happen that forced you to get help even though you really don't want to be helped? Take a minute to write it out below.

4. **Motivating Event:** What happened that made you ask for help now?

    _____

    _____

    _____

    A. Did this motivating event make you want to ask for help?
        Yes   No   Unsure

        Explain your answer: _____

        _____

        _____

    B. Did this motivating event force you to get help even though you really don't want to be helped?
        Yes   No   Unsure

        Explain your answer: _____

        _____

        _____

10

1-7 Step 5: Identifying the Goal

The next step is to identify the goal that you want to accomplish by trying to solve this problem. Effective problem solvers *begin with the end in mind*. In other words, we clearly and vividly imagine what our lives would look like if the problem were solved. In this way, we can develop a clear vision of the outcome that we want to produce.

Let's take a minute and give it a try. Relax and get centered. Now imagine exactly what your life would look like if this problem were solved to your satisfaction. Then write a summary of that vision below.

5. **Goal:** What do you want your life to look like when this problem is solved?

_____

_____

1-8 Step 6: Developing an Action Plan

The next step in addiction-focused problem solving is to develop an action plan. A good action plan consists of three to seven steps that you can take to solve the problem. Each step must be concrete and specific. In other words, you must be able to see yourself doing the things that each step tells you to do. An action step that says: "Start getting along with my spouse" would be too vague and general. A better action step would be to: "Ask my wife to meet with my counselor so we can figure out a way to solve our problems without fighting." Let's give it a try. Take a few minutes and try to figure out a series of three to five steps that you can take to accomplish the goal that you identified in Step 5.

6. **Action Plan:** What steps can you take to start solving this problem?

Step 1 _____

_____

Step 2 _____

_____

Step 3 _____

_____

Step 4 _____

_____

Step 5 _____

_____

Step 6 _____

_____

1-9 Step 7: Identifying the Consequences of *Using* Alcohol or Other Drugs

The next step is to think about what will happen if you decide to start using alcohol or other drugs while trying to solve this problem. If you're addicted, drinking and drugging will stop you dead in your tracks.

Using alcohol and other drugs can do three things that can prevent you from solving the problem.

1. Using alcohol and other drugs can *take away your impulse control*. This means that when you get the urge to stop trying to solve the problem, you'll quit. It also means that if something comes up that seems more interesting or exciting, you'll stop trying to solve the problem and get sidetracked.

2. Using alcohol and other drugs can also cause you to *use poor judgment*. In others words, you'll lose the ability to think things through before you act them out. You won't be able to accurately predict the consequences of the steps you're trying to take to solve your problems.

3. Using alcohol and other drugs can *take away your self-motivation*. You'll tend to become apathetic or lethargic. You'll forget why you wanted to solve the problem in the first place. You'll start to believe that it's just too hard to go through the steps of solving the problem. Then you'll just quit trying.

Take a minute to think back to what has happened when you were drinking and drugging and had important things you had to do or serious problems you needed to solve? Did the drinking and drugging really help? Sure, it might have given you some *temporary relief* from the pain the problem was causing and stress you felt while trying to solve it. But did the booze and drugs really help you solve the problem and make your life better?

Think about what would happen to your ability to solve this problem if you keep using alcohol and other drugs. What's the best thing that could happen? What's the worst thing that could happen? What's the most likely thing that probably will happen? Now take a few moments to answer those questions on the following page.

7. **Consequences of Using Alcohol or Other Drugs:** What will happen if you use alcohol or other drugs to cope with this problem?

    A. **Best:** What's the best thing that could happen if you *use* alcohol or other drugs to cope with this problem?

    _____

    _____

    B. **Worst:** What's the worst thing that could happen if you *use* alcohol or other drugs to cope with this problem?

    _____

    _____

    C. **Most Likely:** What's the most likely thing that probably will happen if you *use* alcohol or other drugs to cope with this problem?

    _____

    _____

1-10 Step 8: Identifying the Consequences of *Not Using* Alcohol or Other Drugs

The next step is to identify the consequences if you don't use alcohol or other drugs to cope with this problem. What's the best thing that could happen if you were to work through the problem-solving process while staying clean and sober? What's the worst that could happen? What's the most likely thing that probably will happen?

Now it's time to compare your answers to this question with your answers to question 7. What gives you the best chance of solving this problem—using alcohol or other drugs or staying sober?

8. **Consequences of Not Using Alcohol or Other Drugs:** What will happen if you *don't use* alcohol or other drugs to cope with this problem?

    A. **Best:** What's the best thing that could happen if you *don't use* alcohol or other drugs to cope with this problem?

    _____

    _____

    B. **Worst**: What's the worst thing that could happen if you *don't use* alcohol or other drugs to cope with this problem?

    _____

    _____

13

C. **Most Likely:** What's the mostly likely thing that probably will happen if you *don't use* alcohol or other drugs to cope with this problem?

_____

_____

1-11 Step 9: Identifying the Best Chance for Success

Now it's time to compare your answers to this question with your answers to question 7 and question 8. What gives you the best chance of solving this problem—using alcohol or other drugs or staying sober?

9. **The Best Chance for Success:** I have the best chance of solving this problem if I . . .
   A. Use alcohol or other drugs while trying to solve the problem.

   B. Stay clean and sober while trying to solve the problem.

   Explain your answer: _____

   _____

   _____

   _____

1-12 Step 10: Identifying Level of Confidence

The final step in addiction-focused problem solving is to evaluate how confident you are that you'll be able to solve this problem while staying clean and sober. Be as honest with yourself as you can. If you can't see yourself solving this problem in a sober and responsible way, you probably won't be able to solve it at all. If this is the case, you'll have to consider one of two things:

   • Maybe you shouldn't be trying to solve this problem right now. There may be some other things that you need to do first in order to develop a stronger commitment to abstinence or a more stable and effective recovery program.
   • Your action plan needs to be revised to make it more realistic.

Take a few minutes to reflect on your current confidence level and then answer the following question.

10. **My Confidence Level:** How strongly do you believe that you can cope with this problem without using alcohol or other drugs?

   Not at all Confident 1——2——3——4——5——6——7——8——9——10 Completely Confident

This brings us to the end of the first exercise in learning the Cognitive Restructuring for Addiction process. In Appendix 1 there is an *Addiction-Focused Problem-Solving Worksheet* that you can use to apply this process to other problems. You have permission to copy this worksheet for your own personal use.

2 Managing Addictive Thinking

2-1 Explanation of Addictive Thinking

As you begin using the Addiction-Focused Problem-Solving Process, you may discover that addictive thoughts start coming to mind that make it difficult to stay focused on the problem-solving process.

Addictive thinking is a common problem. Our addiction caused us to develop habits of addictive thinking that make us want to use alcohol and other drugs. The sole purpose of addictive thinking is to convince us that it's OK to use alcohol or other drugs. Addictive thinking operates on two levels.

- First, addictive thinking causes unnecessary pain and problems.
- Second, the addictive thinking convinces us that the only way to manage the pain or solve the problems is to start using alcohol or other drugs.

These addictive thoughts are cunning, baffling, and powerful. They tend to pop into our minds when we least expect them. Once the addictive thinking process starts, it's hard to stop. The addictive thoughts seem to take on a life of their own.

The following exercise is designed to help you identify and manage the addictive thoughts that can cause unnecessary pain and problems and convince you that it's OK to use alcohol or other drugs to manage the pain and solve the problems.

2-2 Identifying Addictive Thoughts

Instructions: Read the following list of the most commonly used addictive thoughts. Use the ten-point scale to evaluate how true each thought is for you. When you have rated each question, check the box in front of the three addictive thoughts that are most likely to cause you to use alcohol or drugs.

❑ 1. Alcohol and other drugs are safe to use.

Not at all True   1——2——3——4——5——6——7——8——9——10   Completely True

❑ 2. I'll never get addicted or have problems because I use alcohol or other drugs.

Not at all True   1——2——3——4——5——6——7——8——9——10   Completely True

❑ 3. Using alcohol or other drugs is good for me.

Not at all True   1——2——3——4——5——6——7——8——9——10   Completely True

❑ 4. Not using alcohol or other drugs is bad for me.

Not at all True   1——2——3——4——5——6——7——8——9——10   Completely True

❑ 5. Using alcohol or other drugs makes my life worth living.

Not at all True   1——2——3——4——5——6——7——8——9——10   Completely True

❑ 6. Without alcohol or other drugs, my life isn't worth living.

Not at all True   1——2——3——4——5——6——7——8——9——10   Completely True

❑ 7. I need alcohol or other drugs to survive.

Not at all True   1——2——3——4——5——6——7——8——9——10   Completely True

❑ 8. I can't survive without alcohol and other drugs.

Not at all True   1——2——3——4——5——6——7——8——9——10   Completely True

❑ 9. Alcohol and drug-centered lifestyles are good.

Not at all True   1——2——3——4——5——6——7——8——9——10   Completely True

❑ 10. Lifestyles centered on other things that don't involve alcohol or other drugs are bad.

Not at all True   1——2——3——4——5——6——7——8——9——10   Completely True

❑ 11. People who support my use of alcohol or other drugs are my friends.

Not at all True   1——2——3——4——5——6——7——8——9——10   Completely True

❑ 12. People who oppose my using alcohol or other drugs are my enemies.

Not at all True   1——2——3——4——5——6——7——8——9——10   Completely True

❑ 13. I must use alcohol and drugs to have a good life.

Not at all True   1——2——3——4——5——6——7——8——9——10 Completely True

❑ 14. I can't have a good life without using alcohol or other drugs.

Not at all True   1——2——3——4——5——6——7——8——9——10 Completely True

❑ 15. It's OK to use alcohol or other drugs frequently, heavily, and abusively.

Not at all True   1——2——3——4——5——6——7——8——9——10 Completely True

❑ 16. It's not OK to stop using alcohol or other drugs or to use in moderation.

Not at all True   1——2——3——4——5——6——7——8——9——10 Completely True

Note: Appendix 2 contains the *Addictive Thinking Checklist (Long Form)* that contains a list of the thirty-two most common addictive thoughts reported in a survey of the cognitive therapy literature as applied to addiction. This longer list could be helpful in identifying more subtle addictive thoughts that may interfere with your ability to solve problems in a sober and responsible way.

2-3 Examples of Personalized Addictive Thoughts

Instructions: Read the following examples to become familiar with how to personalize an addictive thought. Go back to the exercise in Section 2-2, and write the three addictive thoughts you selected in Section 2-4. Write a personal title and description in your own words. Here are some examples:

Addictive Thought #1:   Alcohol and other drugs are safe to use.

> *Title:*   *It's no big deal.*
>
> *Description: I know I'm using addictive thinking when I start saying to myself that using alcohol or other drugs is no big deal. It's not really dangerous. People are just making it seem more dangerous than it really is to justify hassling people who want to use alcohol and drugs to have a good time.*

Addictive Thought #2:   I'll never get addicted or have problems because I use alcohol or other drugs.

> *Title:*   *I'm the exception.*
>
> *Description: I know I'm using addictive thinking when I start saying to myself that other people may get addicted or have problems because of drinking and drugging, but I'm different. I'm so smart and so careful that it could never happen to me.*

Addictive Thought #3:   Using alcohol or other drugs is good for me.

> *Title:*   *Drinking and drugging works for me.*
>
> *Description: I know I'm using addictive thinking when I start saying to myself that using alcohol and other drugs does good things for me.*

Addictive Thought #4:   Not using alcohol or other drugs is bad for me.

> *Title:*   *Sobriety sucks.*
>
> *Description: I know I'm using addictive thinking when I start saying to myself that if I ever stop using alcohol or other drugs there is no way to have the good times I want to have.*

Addictive Thought #5:   Using alcohol or other drugs makes my life worth living.

> *Title:*   *Living to get high*
>
> *Description: I know I'm using addictive thinking when I start saying to myself that the only thing that makes my life worth living is the ability to get high and to live the good life.*

Addictive Thought #6: Without alcohol or other drugs my life isn't worth living.

> *Title:* *Nothing left*
>
> *Description: I know I'm using addictive thinking when I start saying to myself if I had to stop using alcohol and other drugs there would be nothing of importance left to live for.*

Addictive Thought #7: I need alcohol or other drugs to survive.

> *Title:* *Staying alive*
>
> *Description: I know I'm using addictive thinking when I start saying to myself that the only way I can stay alive and keep from killing myself is to keep using alcohol and other drugs.*

Addictive Thought #8: I can't survive without alcohol and other drugs.

> *Title:* *Can't keep going*
>
> *Description: I know I'm using addictive thinking when I start saying to myself that I can't survive and enjoy life without drinking and drugging.*

Addictive Thought #9: Alcohol and drug-centered lifestyles are good.

> *Title:* *Loving the life*
>
> *Description: I know I'm using addictive thinking when I start saying to myself that the only way to have a good life is to live a drinking-and-drugging lifestyle.*

Addictive Thought #10: Lifestyles centered on other things that don't involve alcohol or other drugs are bad.

> *Title:* *The straight life is boring.*
>
> *Description: I know I'm using addictive thinking when I start saying to myself that there is nothing good to be said about living without alcohol and other drugs.*

Addictive Thought #11: People who support my use of alcohol or other drugs are my friends.

> *Title:* *Loving my brother and sisters in the life*
>
> *Description: I know I'm using addictive thinking when I start saying to myself my drinking buddies, the pushers who give me alcohol and other drugs, and the enablers who allow me to keep drinking and drugging are my true friends.*

Addictive Thought #12: People who oppose my use of alcohol or other drugs are my enemies.

> *Title:*   *Hating sobriety pushers*
>
> *Description: I know I'm using addictive thinking when I start saying to myself that anyone who wants me to stop using alcohol or drugs is my enemy because they want to take the good things in life away from me.*

Addictive Thought #13: I must use alcohol and drugs to have a good life.

> *Title:*   *Getting high is the good life.*
>
> *Description: I know I'm using addictive thinking when I start saying to myself that using alcohol or other drugs, getting high, and being in the lifestyle is the best way to live and the only way I want to live.*

Addictive Thought #14: I can't have a good life without using alcohol or other drugs.

> *Title:*   *Sobriety is for losers.*
>
> *Description: I know I'm using addictive thinking when I start saying to myself that without drinking and drugging I could never enjoy myself or live an exciting lifestyle.*

Addictive Thought #15: It's OK to use alcohol or other drugs frequently, heavily, and abusively.

> *Title:*   *What's wrong with getting high?*
>
> *Description: I know I'm using addictive thinking when I start saying to myself that there's nothing wrong with getting high and getting in trouble as a result.*

Addictive Thought #16: It's not OK to stop using alcohol or other drugs or to use in moderation.

> *Title:*   *Clean and suckered*
>
> *Description: I know I'm using addictive thinking when I start saying to myself that it will be terrible or horrible if I have to stop using alcohol or other drugs.*

2-4 Personalizing Addictive Thoughts

Instructions: Go to the exercise in Section 2-2, and look at the three addictive thoughts you checked. Use these addictive thoughts to complete the following exercise.

First Addictive Thought You Selected
1. What is the first addictive thought you selected? Copy it directly from the *Addictive Thoughts List*.

    _____

    _____

2. Write a *personal title* for this addictive thought that will be easy for you to remember. The title should be no longer than two or three words.

    _____

3. Write a *personal description* for this addictive thought. Make sure the description is a single sentence that begins with the words: I know I'm using addictive thinking when I start saying to myself . . .

    _____

    _____

    _____

Second Addictive Thought You Selected
1. What is the second addictive thought you selected? Copy it directly from the *Addictive Thoughts List*.

    _____

2. Write a *personal title* for this addictive thought that will be easy for you to remember. The title should be no longer than two or three words.

    _____

3. Write a *personal description* for this addictive thought. Make sure the description is a single sentence that begins with the words: *I know I'm using addictive thinking when I start saying to myself* . . .

    _____

    _____

Third Addictive Thought You Selected
1. What is the third addictive thought you selected? Copy it directly from the *Addictive Thoughts List*.

    _____

2. Write a *personal title* for this addictive thought that will be easy for you to remember. The title should be no longer than two or three words.

    _____

3. Write a *personal description* for this addictive thought. Make sure the description is a single sentence that begins with the words: *I know I'm using addictive thinking when I start saying to myself* . . .

_____

_____

_____

Similarities and Differences among the Addictive Thoughts

1. In what ways are these three addictive thoughts similar?

_____

_____

2. In what ways are these three addictive thoughts different?

_____

_____

3. What are the common ideas that link the three addictive thoughts together?

_____

_____

_____

4. Can you see a series of three or four addictive thoughts that you tend to link together in a sequence to convince yourself it's OK to use alcohol and other drugs despite your problems? Write that sequence of thoughts below.

_____

_____

_____

_____

_____

**Go to the next section (2-5) to
learn how to manage these Addictive Thoughts.**

2-5 How to Challenge Addictive Thoughts

As addiction progresses, addictive thinking becomes an automatic and unconscious habit. This means that addictive thoughts pop into our minds automatically and unconsciously. We don't have to do anything special to start thinking addictively. All we have to do is live our lives as we normally do, and the addictive thoughts will come into our minds.

If we want to recover, we have to become skilled at recognizing our addictive thoughts as soon as they enter our minds. Then we have to learn how to turn them off by challenging our addictive thinking with sober and responsible thinking. Fortunately, there are proven and effective ways for doing this. Here are the steps to the process.

Step 1: Recognize addictive thinking as soon as it starts.

In order to do this you have to learn the most common addictive thoughts and go through the process of personalizing them. Then you have to identify the situations that are most likely to trigger or activate those thoughts. Then you need to get in the habit of doing a daily inventory in which you consciously evaluate what addictive thoughts have entered your mind.

Step 2: Acknowledge to yourself that you are using addictive thinking.

Say this to yourself: "This is an addictive thought. I'm starting to use addictive thinking."

Step 3: Acknowledge where these thoughts will take you.

Say this to yourself: "This isn't good. If I allow these addictive thoughts to stay in my mind, I'll start believing them. And if I start believing them, I'll eventually convince myself to start using alcohol or other drugs."

Step 4: Write the addictive thought.

Once you write the thought on a sheet of paper, it will become real to you. It will also allow you to separate the thought from who you are. Say this to yourself: "This is an automatic addictive thought. At one time I thought it was true. At this moment I can choose to either believe it, or challenge it and force myself to think in a different way that will support my commitment to sobriety and responsibility."

Step 5: Write down a rational thought that directly challenges the addictive thought.

Don't be subtle. You have to be very simple and direct. If the addictive thought is: "Alcohol and drugs are good for me." You must challenge it by writing down: "No they're not. That's a lie. Alcohol and drugs are not good for me—they are bad for me and here's the proof." Then you need to write all the past experiences that prove to you that using alcohol and other drugs is not good for you; that it is, in fact, dangerous and destructive.

Step 6: Repeat the rational challenge and evidence to yourself with strong emotion.

The only way to turn off an addictive thought is to put a lot of emotional energy behind the rational challenge. Think of your addictive thinking as an enemy trying to hurt or kill you. Remember all the pain and problems that were caused by drinking and drugging. Imagine that your addictive thoughts are forcing you to experience even worse pain and problems. Be aware that your addiction is lying to you and trying to trick you. Let yourself get angry and upset. Then tie these feelings and emotions into the rational challenge.

Yell it out in your mind: "No, it's not true. That's a lie. If I keep thinking this way, I'll get dragged back into my addiction. Look at the pain and problems my addiction has already caused me. It's lies like this that have caused the pain. This way of thinking is not true. Here's why . . ." Then go over the evidence that proves the addictive thoughts are not true.

**Go to Section (2-6) and
read examples of how to challenge Addictive Thoughts.**

2-6 Examples of How to Challenge Addictive Thoughts

Instructions: Below is a list of examples of how to challenge the sixteen most common addictive thoughts. Read the entire list. Then find the three addictive thoughts that you selected and review those rational challenges very carefully.

1. **Alcohol and other drugs are safe to use.**
   Rational Challenge: No, they're not. Heavy and regular drinking can cause serious health problems. Getting drunk puts me in high risk of doing dumb things, embarrassing myself, and having accidents. There is no such thing as safe illegal drugs; illegal drugs are not produced to pharmacy standards. I have no way of knowing what's really in the drugs or how strong they are. This increases my risk of getting poisoned, overdosing, and getting sick. Buying illegal drugs puts me at risk of getting arrested and forces me to deal with criminals who will cheat or rob me the first chance they get. So using alcohol and other drugs is not safe. It's dangerous.

2. **I'll never have problems or get addicted because I use alcohol or other drugs.**
   Rational Challenge: That's not true. Anyone who uses alcohol or other drugs regularly and heavily runs the risk of getting addicted. Anyone who drinks and drugs regularly and heavily runs the risk of getting in trouble. Most heavy drinkers and drug users do eventually get into trouble. Look at what's already happened to me. I've embarrassed myself in front of friends when I was drunk or stoned. I've spent too much money. I've broken the law and run the risk of getting arrested. If I keep drinking and drugging, these sorts of problems will just keep getting worse.

3. **Using alcohol or other drugs is good for me.**
   Rational Challenge: No, it's not. Using alcohol makes me feel good. It is not good for me. There is a big difference. When I start drinking or using drugs, my judgment and impulse control is affected. I start doing dumb things that end up hurting me. It seems like a good idea at the time, but there's always a price to pay. I also tend to do things without thinking that cause me a lot of pain and problems. I may feel good for a little while when I'm drinking and drugging, but there is a lot of pain and problems that follow me back to the sober world.

4. **Not using alcohol or other drugs is bad for me.**
   Rational Challenge: No, it isn't. Not using alcohol and other drugs makes me feel bad, but it isn't bad for me. There's a big difference between the two. When I stop drinking and drugging, a lot of the painful feelings that I medicated start to come back. It also becomes harder to keep from seeing the problems that I've created in my life. These things hurt, but it is good pain that can signal me that I need to live my life in a more responsible and effective way.

5. **Using alcohol or other drugs makes my life worth living.**
   Rational Challenge: No, it doesn't. Alcohol and drugs create the illusion that I have the good life. There are two parts to this illusion. First, the drugs make me feel better without having to think better, act better, or live my life in a better way. Therefore it's easy to believe the alcohol and drugs are helping me have a good life, when they are just taking away the painful feelings that would force me to deal with the growing prob-

lems I'm having in my life. Second, I've surrounded myself with other people who use alcohol and other drugs regularly and heavily. When we get together, we keep telling one another how great it is to drink and drug and how foolish people are who live the straight life. But in reality, we're not doing so well. Our lives are pretty messed up and we tell our war stories to give us an excuse to keep drinking and drugging. Except for the times when the booze and drugs are making me feel the way I want to feel, there's a lot of pain and problems that go along with drinking and drugging. I spend too much money; I end up lying, cheating, and stealing to get booze and drugs; and I've let down a lot of good people and driven friends and family out of my life.

6. **Without alcohol or other drugs, my life isn't worth living.**
Rational Challenge: This is easy to believe but it just isn't true. I've met people in recovery who seem to be happy. They're dealing with life effectively. They have problems, but they seem to be able to handle them without falling apart. They're part of a community of recovering people. They don't get into trouble with the law, they tend to manage their money more responsibly, they treat people better, and they seem to know how to be at peace with themselves. I know I can have these things happen for me if I just stop drinking and drugging one day at a time, follow the steps of recovery, and reach out for help whenever I feel depressed or feel like starting to drink and use drugs again. I've already had some pretty good days. My life will never be perfect, but I can already see that I can make it better than it was when I was drinking or drugging.

7. **I need alcohol or other drugs to survive.**
Rational Challenge: Alcohol and drugs won't help me survive. They're setting me up for pain and problems. There have already been times when I've gotten hurt and nearly killed because of some of the stupid things I did while drinking and drugging. When I'm using, the only thing I care about is using. I let everything else go down the tubes. My life shrinks into a dirty little mud puddle.

8. **I can't survive without alcohol and other drugs.**
Rational Challenge: This definitely isn't true. I've already had some periods of time in my life when I wasn't drinking and drugging. I didn't crumble into a pile of dust and get blown away. There were some good moments and some difficult moments when I was sober, but I got through them. I know that I'll be in a better position to manage my life if I'm clean and sober than if I'm drinking and drugging. Sobriety is my lifeline to survival. Using alcohol and drugs is a pathway to pain, problems, illness, and death. I need to remember this every time I feel discouraged in my sobriety.

9. **Alcohol-centered and drug-centered lifestyles are good.**
Rational Challenge: Alcohol-centered and drug-centered lifestyles are not good. In order to keep drinking and drugging, I have put myself in some pretty disgusting places and have dealt with some pretty dangerous and repulsive people.

10. **Lifestyles centered on other things that don't involve alcohol or drugs are bad.**
Rational Challenge: There are better ways of living than being tied to drinking and drugging. There are a lot of good people doing things that are important, meaningful, and enjoyable. Sober and responsible living is the best way to build a better life.

26

Drinking and drugging is a dead-end street that leads only one place. It leads me to pain, problems, loneliness, and illness. It will eventually kill me. When I stop drinking and using drugs, I am free to build a way of life that is healthier, happier, and capable of bringing me a sense of meaning and purpose.

11. **People who support my use of alcohol or other drugs are my friends.**
    Rational Challenge: People who support my alcohol and drug use are not my friends. They pretend to be my friends but they are really not. Some of these people are drinking buddies. They need someone to drink with and I happen to be convenient. But if I ever stopped drinking and drugging they'd want nothing to do with me. They'd find someone else to get high with and probably wouldn't even miss me. Other people support my drinking and drugging because they get rich off of me. I have friends who sell me drugs and bartenders and liquor store clerks who sell me the booze. They don't care about me. They care about the money I spend. If I ever stopped spending money on alcohol and drugs they'd never want to see me again.

12. **People who oppose my using alcohol or other drugs are my enemies.**
    Rational Challenge: No, they are not. I see them as enemies because I want them to leave me alone so I can keep drinking and drugging. The people who are most against my drinking are those who love and care about me the most. They can see the pain and problems that alcohol and other drugs are bringing to my life. They can see that I'm getting lost in a lifestyle of addiction. They don't want to lose me and they can see that booze and drugs are killing me. They care about me enough to take a stand and tell me that I need to stop. If they didn't love and care about me, they wouldn't go out of their way to try and help me.

13. **I must use alcohol and drugs to have a good life.**
    Rational Challenge: This is not true. The only thing using alcohol and drugs does for me is it makes me feel euphoric and high. This drug-induced euphoria makes me believe that I'm living a good life, when in reality I'm living a miserable, disgusting, and embarrassing life. If it weren't for my ability to use alcohol and drugs to deal with the painful realities of my addictive lifestyle, I wouldn't be able to tolerate the pain. Drinking and drugging aren't giving me a good life. They are giving me an anesthetic so I don't feel the pain as I flush my life down the toilet.

14. **I can't have a good life without using alcohol or other drugs.**
    Rational Challenge: That's not true. I can have a very good life without using alcohol or other drugs. As a matter of fact, if I keep drinking and drugging, I won't be able to live a good life. Look at all the pain and problems my drinking and drugging has caused. Since I quit, life has been a mixed bag. I've had good days and bad days, but overall things are getting better and I'm learning to handle my life better. I know that other people have a good life in sobriety. I know that I can too.

15. **It's OK to use alcohol or other drugs frequently, heavily, and abusively.**
    Rational Challenge: No, it's not. Using any amount of alcohol and drugs is dangerous for me. Look at all of the times I've tried to cut back and control my using. Each time I failed. I went back to using more than I intended. I went back to using so much

that I started having problems again. To believe that heavy drinking and drugging is a good thing is stupid. Heavy drinking and drugging is a bad thing. It's a serious problem that could destroy my life.

16. **It's not OK to stop using alcohol or other drugs.**
    Rational Challenge: That's not true. It's perfectly OK to stop using alcohol and other drugs. As a matter of fact, if I want to solve my problems and get my life back, staying clean and sober is the only way to do it. It would be stupid to keep drinking and drugging after experiencing the kinds of problems I've experienced. The only sane and sensible thing to do is to stop drinking and drugging completely and do whatever is necessary to stay stopped.

**Go to Section (2-7) to
learn how to challenge Addictive Thoughts.**

2-7 Challenging Addictive Thoughts

Instructions: Look at each of the addictive thoughts that you identified in the exercise in Section 2-4, and fill in the information requested below:

Addictive Thought #1 Title: _____

    1.   I know I'm using addictive thinking when I start saying to myself . . .

_____

_____

    2.   I can challenge this addictive thought (convince myself it's not true) by saying . . .

_____

_____

_____

Addictive Thought #2 Title: _____

    1.   I know I'm using addictive thinking when I start saying to myself . . .

_____

_____

    2.   I can challenge this addictive thought (convince myself it's not true) by saying . . .

_____

_____

_____

Addictive Thought #3 Title: _____

    1.   I know I'm using addictive thinking when I start saying to myself . . .

_____

_____

    2.   I can challenge this addictive thought (convince myself it's not true) by saying . . .

_____

_____

_____

> **Go to Section (2-8) to**
> **use Inner Dialogues to challenge Addictive Thoughts.**

2-8 Using Inner Dialogues to Manage Addictive Thoughts

Instructions: Addicted people have an inner conflict between their addictive self (the automatic addictive thinking that tries to convince them to use alcohol and other drugs) and their sober self (their newly learned sober thinking that tries to convince them to stay sober and keep working their recovery program). One way to manage these thoughts is to have a conscious inner conversation or dialogue between the addictive self and the sober self. This can be done by using the following format.

1. **When I start using Addictive Thought #1, my *addictive self* says:**

    _____

    _____

2. **Then my *sober self* argues back by saying:**

    _____

    _____

3. **Then my *addictive self* argues back by saying:**

    _____

    _____

4. **Then my *sober self* argues back by saying:**

    _____

    _____

5. **Then my *addictive self* argues back by saying:**

    _____

    _____

6. **Then my *sober self* argues back by saying:**

    _____

    _____

7. **Then my *addictive self* argues back by saying:**

    _____

    _____

8. **Then my *sober self* argues back by saying:**

    _____

    _____

9. Then my *addictive self* argues back by saying:

_____

_____

10. Then my *sober self* argues back by saying:

_____

_____

11. Then my *addictive self* argues back by saying:

_____

_____

12. Then my *sober self* argues back by saying:

_____

_____

13. Then my *addictive self* argues back by saying:

_____

_____

14. Then my *sober self* argues back by saying:

_____

_____

15. Then my *addictive self* argues back by saying:

_____

_____

16. What were the most powerful sober thoughts that were able to turn off or defeat these addictive thoughts?

A. _____

_____

B. _____

_____

C. _____

_____

Go to \Section (2-9) to
learn how to manage Addictive Feelings.

2-9 Identifying and Managing Addictive Thoughts

Instructions: Go to the exercise in Section 2-8 and copy the most powerful sober thoughts that you used in the dialogue with your addictive self in the spaces below. Try to eliminate duplications and write those thoughts in clear and powerful language that will be easy for you to remember and use in the future.

1. **Sober Thought #1**
    Title _____

    Self-Talk Statement _____

    _____

    _____

    How confident are you that using this sober statement can turn off your addictive thinking?

    Not at all Confident 1——2——3——4——5——6——7——8——9——10 Completely Confident

2. **Sober Thought #2**
    Title _____

    Self-Talk Statement _____

    _____

    _____

    How confident are you that using this sober statement can turn off your addictive thinking?

    Not at all Confident 1——2——3——4——5——6——7——8——9——10 Completely Confident

3. **Sober Thought #3**
    Title _____

    Self-Talk Statement _____

    _____

    _____

    How confident are you that using this sober statement can turn off your addictive thinking?

    Not at all Confident 1——2——3——4——5——6——7——8——9——10 Completely Confident

3 Managing Addictive Feelings

3-1 Select a Thought that Causes Strong Feelings

Look at your personal list of addictive thoughts in Section 2-7 that you are learning to manage and fill in the information requested below:

A. **Title:** _____

B. **Description:** I know I'm using addictive thinking when I start thinking . . .

_____

_____

C. **Feeling Statement:** When I am saying this to myself I tend to feel . . .

_____

_____

3-2 Use the Feeling Checklist

Review the feeling list below, and check all the feelings that you experience when you are using this addictive thought. Answer the following clarifying questions.

When you are experiencing this addictive thought do you tend to feel . . .

A. ❑ *Strong*　　or ❑ *Weak*? How intense is the feeling? (0–10) _____

Why do you rate it this way_____

B. ❑ *Angry*　　or ❑ *Caring*? How intense is the feeling? (0–10) _____

Why do you rate it this way? _____

C. ❑ *Happy*　　or ❑ *Sad*? How intense is the feeling? (0–10) _____

Why do you rate it this way? _____

D. ❑ *Safe*　　or ❑ *Threatened*? How intense is the feeling? (0–10) _____

Why do you rate it this way? _____

E. ❑ *Fulfilled*　　or ❑ *Frustrated*? How intense is the feeling? (0–10) _____

Why do you rate it this way? _____

F. ❑ *Proud*　　or ❑ *Ashamed*? How intense is the feeling? (0–10) _____

Why do you rate it this way? _____

G. ❑ *Lonely*　　or ❑ *Connected*? How intense is the feeling? (0–10) _____

Why do you rate it this way? _____

3-3 Select the Three Strongest Feelings

What are the three strongest feelings you experience when using this addictive thought?

Feeling #1: _____

Why did you choose this feeling? _____

Feeling #2: _____

Why did you choose this feeling? _____

Feeling #3: _____

Why did you choose this feeling? _____

3-4 Select a Feeling You Want to Learn How to Manage

Review the three feelings that you identified above. Select the feeling that you want to learn how to manage more effectively. _____

A.   What are you *thinking* that makes you feel this way?

_____

_____

B.   What is another way of *thinking* that could help you manage this feeling better?

_____

_____

C.   What are you *doing* that makes you feel this way?

_____

_____

D.   What else could you *do* to manage this feeling better?

_____

_____

3-5 Recognize the Feeling Quickly

What can you do to recognize this feeling as soon as it occurs?

_____

_____

Here are some things that other people have found helpful:
1. Plan ahead to anticipate situations that are likely to cause this feeling.
2. Stay centered and aware of the rise and fall of inner feelings.
3. Take a deep breath and notice when I am starting to have this feeling.

3-6 Clarify the Feeling

What can you do to clarify what you are feeling?

_____

_____

Here are some things that other people have found helpful:
1. Find words that describe what I'm feeling (using the feeling checklist, if needed).
2. Rate the intensity of my feelings using a ten-point scale.
3. Consciously acknowledge the feeling and its intensity by saying to myself, "Right now I'm feeling _____ and it's okay to be feeling this way."

3-7 Talk to Supportive People

Who can you talk to about the feeling to help you manage it better?

_____

_____

Here are some things that other people have found helpful:
1. Ask my therapist, therapy group, or support group who I could talk with about this feeling.
2. Call that person as soon as I recognize that I'm having the feeling.
3. Talk about what I am feeling with my therapist, therapy group, or at a Twelve Step meeting.

3-8 Find the Cause of the Feeling

What can you do to figure out what is causing you to feel this way?

_____

_____

Here are some things that other people have found helpful:
1. Identify *what I'm thinking* that's making me feel this way and ask myself, "How can I change my thinking in a way that will make me feel better?"
2. Identify *what I'm doing* that's making me feel this way and ask myself, "How can I change what I'm doing in a way that will make me feel better?"
3. Recognize the *mistaken* beliefs that are triggering the feeling.

3-9 Control Impulses to Act Out

What can you do to stop from reacting to this feeling without thinking it through?

_____

_____

Here are some things that other people have found helpful:

1. Call a time out before the feeling becomes unmanageable.

2. Use an immediate relaxation technique to bring down the intensity of the feeling.

3. Consciously stop the urge to react automatically to the feeling without thinking it through.

4. Recognize and resist urges to create problems or to hurt myself or others in an attempt to make myself feel better.

5. Recognize my resistance to doing things that would help me or my situation and *motivate myself* to do those things despite the resistance.

4 Managing Addictive Behaviors

Instructions: Managing automatic addictive behaviors involves: (1) learning how to recognize and stop the urges to put yourself around people, places, and things that promote the use of alcohol and other drugs; and (2) motivating yourself to use sober and responsible behaviors that put you around people, places, and things that will support sobriety and responsibility. You can learn how to do this by completing the following process:

4-1 Identifying an Addictive Thought

Look at the addictive thought you are learning to manage and fill in the information requested below.

A. **Title:** _____

B. **Description:** I know I'm using addictive thinking when I start saying to myself . . .

_____

_____

4-2 Identifying Self-Destructive Urges

When using this addictive thought, what do you have an urge to do that would make things worse in the long run?

_____

_____

A. Notice there is *a part of you that wants to use self-destructive behavior* that will make things worse? Tell me about that part.

_____

_____

B. Notice there is *a part of you that wants to resist the urge to use this self-destructive behavior* and wants to find a more effective way of managing this addictive thought? Tell me about that part.

_____

_____

4-3 Identifying Constructive Urges

If you want to manage this urge more effectively, what part of yourself do you need to listen to and why?

_____

_____

4-4 Writing an Action Statement

What do you usually do to act out this addictive thought?

_____

_____

4-5 Completing the Self-Defeating Behavior Checklist

Keeping this addictive thought in mind, read the following list of *Self-Defeating Behaviors*, and check any behaviors you might use that could make things worse or cause you to use alcohol or drugs.

❑ A.   **Procrastinating:** I use old self-defeating behaviors that make things worse by:
   ❑   (1)   Finding excuses or reasons for not doing it now.
   ❑   (2)   Getting too busy with other things to do it now.
   ❑   (3)   See other things as more important.
   ❑   (4)   Convince myself that nothing is wrong.
   ❑   (5)   Convincing myself that I'm too weak and helpless.

❑ B.   **Mismanaging:** I use old self-defeating behaviors that makes things worse by:
   ❑   (1)   Reacting without thinking it through.
   ❑   (2)   Trying to handle it by myself without asking for help.
   ❑   (3)   Feeling helpless and expecting others to do it for me.
   ❑   (4)   Constantly changing my mind and not sticking to a plan.
   ❑   (5)   Ignoring the situation so it doesn't bother me.
   ❑   (6)   Getting scared and using my fear as an excuse.

4-6 Identifying Personal Self-Defeating Behaviors

What are three self-defeating behaviors that you tend to use when acting out on this addictive thought? It is important for you to write the descriptions in you own words.

A.   **Self-Defeating Behavior #1:** _____

_____

Why did you choose this behavior? _____

_____

B.   **Self-Defeating Behavior #2:** _____

_____

Why did you choose this behavior? _____

_____

C.   **Self-Defeating Behavior #3:** _____

_____

Why did you choose this behavior? _____

_____

4-7 Identifying a Self-Defeating Behavior to Manage

Select the self-defeating behavior that you want to learn how to manage more effectively?

_____

_____

A. What makes you want to use this self-defeating behavior?

_____

_____

B. What do you want to accomplish by using it?

_____

_____

C. Does this self-defeating behavior get you what you want?

❑ Yes   ❑ No   ❑ Unsure   Why did you answer this way?

_____

_____

D. When you use this self-defeating behavior, how do other people usually react to you?

_____

_____

E. Does the way that other people react to you make it harder or easier to effectively manage this addictive thought?

❑ Harder   ❑ Easier   ❑ Unsure   Why did you answer this way?

_____

_____

F. How could other people react to you in a way that would help you to stay away from alcohol or drugs?

_____

_____

4-8 Identifying a New Way of Behaving

What is another way of behaving that could help you manage this situation more effectively?

_____

_____

A. How can you motivate yourself to manage this addictive thought in this new and more effective way?

_____

_____

B. How could you invite other people to help you deal more effectively with this addictive thought?

_____

_____

_____

**Go to the next page to
learn how to tie together everything that you have
learned about managing this Addictive Thought.**

5 Integrating Personal Reactions

This exercise will help you put together everything that you have learned from completing the previous exercises on managing addictive thoughts, feelings, urges, and actions. Before completing this exercise, review the exercises in Sections 1–4. Take time to reflect on each answer. See what you were really saying in each answer. See how the answers to different questions are somehow related or connected to other answers. Complete the questions in the table below.

1. Select an addictive thought that you want to learn how to manage, and fill in the information below.

    A. **Title:** _____

    B. **Description:** I know I'm using addictive thinking when I start saying . . .

    _____

    _____

2a. When you use this addictive thought what do you tend to think?	2b. What is another way of thinking that will help you better manage this addictive thought?
_____ _____ _____ _____ _____ _____	_____ _____ _____ _____ _____ _____
3a. When you use this addictive thought, what do you feel? How do you mismanage those feelings?	3b. What is another way to manage these feelings that will help you deal better with this addictive thought?
_____ _____ _____ _____	_____ _____ _____ _____

4a. When you use this addictive thought, what do you have an urge to do?	4b. What is another way of managing this urge that will help you deal with this addictive thought more effectively?
_____ _____ _____ _____	_____ _____ _____ _____
5a. When you use this addictive thought, what do you usually do?	5b. What are some other things you could do that will help you deal with this addictive thought more effectively?
_____ _____ _____ _____	_____ _____ _____ _____
6a. When you use this addictive thought, how do other people usually react to you?	6b. How could you invite other people to react to you in a way that will help you deal with this addictive thought more effectively?
_____ _____ _____ _____	_____ _____ _____ _____

7. Most Important Thing Learned

What is the most important thing that you learned by completing this exercise?

_____

_____

This exercise stops here.

A Final Word

It is possible to learn how to manage addictive thinking. But it's not easy. The process requires consistent work usually with the help of other people, including a trained addiction professional and members of a self-help support group such as Alcoholics Anonymous or other Twelve Step programs.

It's normal to periodically fall back into old addictive ways of thinking and managing feelings. This is frustrating, but it's not the end of the world. If you recognize what is happening, you can stop the old addictive ways of thinking and acting and make a new commitment to continue to use sober and responsible ways of coping with your life.

If you find you have a tendency to relapse back into alcohol and drug use, there are other resources that are available to help you.

The *Relapse Prevention Counseling Workbook* provides a system for identifying and managing high-risk situations that activate craving. The *Relapse Prevention Therapy Workbook* shows you how to identify and manage core personality and lifestyle problems that can make drinking and using drugs seem like a positive option later in recovery after you have developed a stable recovery plan.

I offer you my best wishes as you continue your journey of recovery.

—*Terence T. Gorski*

Appendix 1
Addiction-Focused Problem-Solving Worksheet

1. **Problem:** What's going on in your life that's making you unhappy? One problem that's making me unhappy is . . .

   _____

   _____

2. **When the Problem Started:** When did this first become a problem? This first became a problem when . . .

   _____

   _____

3. **Past Attempts to Solve the Problem:** What are the three most important things that you've done in the past to try to solve this problem, and what happened as a result?

   A. The first thing I did to try to solve this problem was . . .

   _____

   _____

   As a result of doing this, the problem . . .

   ❏ Got better   ❏ Stayed the same   ❏ Got worse   Explain:

   _____

   _____

   B. The second thing I did to try to solve this problem was . . .

   _____

   _____

   As a result of doing this, the problem . . .

   ❏ Got better   ❏ Stayed the same   ❏ Got worse   Explain:

   _____

   _____

   C. The third thing I did to try to solve this problem was . . .

   _____

   _____

As a result of doing this, the problem . . .

❑ Got better   ❑ Stayed the same   ❑ Got worse   Explain:

_____

_____

4. Motivating Event: What happened that made you ask for help now?

_____

_____

_____

A. Did this motivating event make you want to ask for help?

❑ Yes   ❑ No   ❑ Unsure   Explain:

_____

_____

B. Did this motivating event force you to get help even though you really don't want to be helped?

❑ Yes   ❑ No   ❑ Unsure   Explain:

_____

_____

5. Goal: What do you want your life to look like when this problem is solved?

_____

_____

6. Action Plan: What steps can you take to start solving this problem?

Step 1_____

_____

Step 2_____

_____

Step 3_____

_____

Step 4_____

_____

Step 5_____

_____

Step 6_____

_____

Step 7_____

_____

7. **Consequences of Using Alcohol or Other Drugs:** What will happen if you use alcohol or other drugs to cope with this problem?

    A. **Best:** What's the best thing that could happen if you *use* alcohol or other drugs to cope with this problem?

    _____

    _____

    B. **Worst:** What's the worst thing that could happen if you *use* alcohol or other drugs to cope with this problem?

    _____

    _____

    C. **Most Likely:** What's the most likely thing that probably will happen if you *use* alcohol or other drugs to cope with this problem?

    _____

    _____

8. **Consequences of Not Using Alcohol or Other Drugs:** What will happen if you *don't use* alcohol or other drugs to cope with this problem?

    A. **Best:** What's the best thing that could happen if you *don't use* alcohol or other drugs to cope with this problem?

    _____

    _____

    B. **Worst:** What's the worst thing that could happen if you *don't use* alcohol or other drugs to cope with this problem?

    _____

    _____

    C. **Most Likely:** What's the most likely thing that probably will happen if you *don't use* alcohol or other drugs to cope with this problem?

    _____

    _____

9. **The Best Chance for Success:** I have the best chance of solving this problem if I:

   A. Use alcohol or other drugs while trying to solve the problem.

   B. Stay clean and sober while trying to solve the problem.

   Explain your answer: _____

   _____

10. **Confidence Level:** How strongly do you believe that you can cope with this problem without using alcohol or other drugs?

   Not at all Confident 1——2——3——4——5——6——7——8——9——10 Completely Confident

Appendix 2
Addictive-Thinking Checklist (Long Form)

❑ 1. I have a right to use alcohol and other drugs.

Not at all True   1——2——3——4——5——6——7——8——9——10   Completely True

❑ 2. Nobody has the right to tell me to stop using alcohol and other drugs.

Not at all True   1——2——3——4——5——6——7——8——9——10   Completely True

❑ 3. Alcohol and other drugs are safe.

Not at all True   1——2——3——4——5——6——7——8——9——10   Completely True

❑ 4. I'll never get addicted or have serious problems with alcohol or other drugs!

Not at all True   1——2——3——4——5——6——7——8——9——10   Completely True

❑ 5. Alcohol and other drugs are good for me.

Not at all True   1——2——3——4——5——6——7——8——9——10   Completely True

❑ 6. I usually feel good when I'm using alcohol and other drugs.

Not at all True   1——2——3——4——5——6——7——8——9——10   Completely True

❑ 7. I rarely feel bad or have problems when I'm using alcohol and drugs.

Not at all True   1——2——3——4——5——6——7——8——9——10   Completely True

❑ 8. Alcohol and other drugs let me do things that I can't do without them.

Not at all True   1——2——3——4——5——6——7——8——9——10   Completely True

❑ 9. Alcohol and other drugs make it easy for me to deal with people.

Not at all True   1——2——3——4——5——6——7——8——9——10   Completely True

❑ 10. Alcohol and drugs let me handle pain and solve problems that I couldn't otherwise.

Not at all True   1——2——3——4——5——6——7——8——9——10   Completely True

❑ 11. Not using alcohol and other drugs stops me from doing things that I could do if I were using.

Not at all True   1——2——3——4——5——6——7——8——9——10   Completely True

❏ 12. Not using alcohol and other drugs makes it hard for me to deal with people and build relationships.

Not at all True   1——2——3——4——5——6——7——8——9——10   Completely True

❏ 13. I usually feel bad and have a lot of pain and problems when I'm not using alcohol and other drugs.

Not at all True   1——2——3——4——5——6——7——8——9——10   Completely True

❏ 14. Not using alcohol and other drugs causes me pain and problems that I wouldn't have if I were using.

Not at all True   1——2——3——4——5——6——7——8——9——10   Completely True

❏ 15. Not using alcohol and other drugs is bad for me.

Not at all True   1——2——3——4——5——6——7——8——9——10   Completely True

❏ 16. It's OK to use alcohol and other drugs frequently and heavily.

Not at all True   1——2——3——4——5——6——7——8——9——10   Completely True

❏ 17. A lifestyle that centers on using alcohol and other drugs is exciting.

Not at all True   1——2——3——4——5——6——7——8——9——10   Completely True

❏ 18. A lifestyle that is not centered on alcohol and other drugs is boring.

Not at all True   1——2——3——4——5——6——7——8——9——10   Completely True

❏ 19. I must use alcohol and other drugs to have a good life.

Not at all True   1——2——3——4——5——6——7——8——9——10   Completely True

❏ 20. I can't have the good life without drinking and drugging.

Not at all True   1——2——3——4——5——6——7——8——9——10   Completely True

❏ 21. Using alcohol and other drugs makes my life worth living.

Not at all True   1——2——3——4——5——6——7——8——9——10   Completely True

❏ 22. Without alcohol and other drugs, my life isn't worth living.

Not at all True   1——2——3——4——5——6——7——8——9——10   Completely True

❏ 23. I need alcohol and other drugs to deal with the pain and problems in my life.

Not at all True   1——2——3——4——5——6——7——8——9——10   Completely True

❏ 24. Without alcohol and other drugs, I wouldn't be able to cope with the pain and problems in my life.

Not at all True   1——2——3——4——5——6——7——8——9——10   Completely True

❏ 25. I don't have problems because I use alcohol and other drugs. I use alcohol and drugs to cope with my problems.

Not at all True   1——2——3——4——5——6——7——8——9——10   Completely True

❏ 26. I am in control of my alcohol and other drug use; it does not control me.

Not at all True   1——2——3——4——5——6——7——8——9——10   Completely True

❏ 27. I can stop any time I want to, I just don't want to because there's really no good reason to stop.

Not at all True   1——2——3——4——5——6——7——8——9——10   Completely True

❏ 28. I must control my alcohol and other drug use, or I will be no good.

Not at all True   1——2——3——4——5——6——7——8——9——10   Completely True

❏ 29. I need alcohol and other drugs to survive.

Not at all True   1——2——3——4——5——6——7——8——9——10   Completely True

❏ 30. I can't survive without using alcohol and other drugs.

Not at all True   1——2——3——4——5——6——7——8——9——10   Completely True

❏ 31. People who support my use of alcohol and other drugs are friends.

Not at all True   1——2——3——4——5——6——7——8——9——10   Completely True

❏ 32. People who criticize my use of alcohol and other drugs are enemies.

Not at all True   1——2——3——4——5——6——7——8——9——10   Completely True

Notes

Notes